Mercury and Sirius

Debbie Garcia-Bengochea

Published by:
Simply Pets Books
620 South Orcas Street #80651
Seattle, Washington 98108

books@simplypetslifestyle.com
https://www.simplypetslifestyle.com

Editor: Lillie Ammann
Photos & Art: Debbie Garcia-Bengochea
Cover: Aundrea Hernandez
Layout: Jan McClintock

ISBN (hardcover): 978-1-7341932-0-6
ISBN (paperback): 978-1-7341932-1-3

Find this great book and others at Simply Pets (www.simplypetslifestyle.com).

Lisa and the Pet Detectives by Lisa Smith Putnam

Coming soon:

Running Silently by Betsy Waterman

Chef Christophe's Cookbook

Dedication

For all of the children and their families who have loved and been loved by Gentle Carousel Miniature Therapy Horses over the past two decades.

Thank you to the Ingram Family for your love and support.

Mercury made his first new friend when he was one day old.

He walked up to Sirius, this fearless little foal,

and touched the fluffy puppy on the end of his nose.

He knew at once they were so much alike.

Mercury loves to see how fast he can run.

Sirius loves to nap on the porch in the sun.

Living on a farm is always fun, when two friends are so much alike.

Mercury thinks hay is a wonderful treat.

Sirius doesn't think hay is fun to eat.

But what a soft place to fall asleep, when two friends are so much alike.

On hot summer days, Sirius soaks in the pool.

Mercury splashes, jumps, and runs right through.

Can you think of a better way to stay cool when two friends are so much alike?

Mercury's little hooves are shiny and tough.

Sirius has big paws with soft, white fluff.

Four legs each run fast enough when two friends are so much alike.

In a sunny green pasture Mercury enjoys his day.

On a soft bed by the fireplace Sirius longs to stay.

They go inside to rest and outside to play, two friends who are so much alike.

Mercury is a funny and confident guy.

Sirius is serious and a little bit shy.

They help each other give new things a try, two friends who are so much alike.

Sirius has a sister; she is fuzzy and white.

Mercury's sister Magic is as black as night.

When they all grow up, they will be the same height.

These friends are so much alike!

A blue-eyed horse and a brown-eyed pup,

big floppy ears or ears straight up.

They can see the whole world from their pickup truck, two friends who are so much alike.

Mercury whinnies when he meets someone new.

Sirius barks like all puppies do.

They both mean, "Hello, how are you?"

These two friends are so much alike.

How much fun do you think it would be,

if we were all like Sirius and Mercury?

They may be different but only see the ways they are alike.

We could look to our left and look to our right,

smile at someone new, and we just might

find a new friend today!

Yay. Neigh. Woof.

Mercury and Sirius

Sirius is a Maremma sheepdog, a live-stock guardian breed from Italy. Maremma sheepdogs have been traced back 2,000 years to the Italian region of Abruzzo where they protected herds of sheep from thieves and wild animals. They are usually solid white dogs. Sirius has five white sisters and his parents and grandparents are also totally white. But not Sirius, he was born with spots.

When Sirius was two months old, Mercury was born on the farm. Mercury is a blue-eyed miniature horse. He has spots too, and an unusual color pattern with three white legs and one dark leg, one white ear and one dark ear.

Mercury and Sirius became instant friends. Maybe it was because they were both babies at the same time. They started playing together and when they got tired, sleeping together. If Mercury walked inside the farmhouse, Sirius was not far behind. Mercury's mother did not worry about Sirius spending time with her foal. On the farm where they live, a team of adult Maremma sheepdogs help protect the miniature horses, and the horses consider the dogs part of their herd.

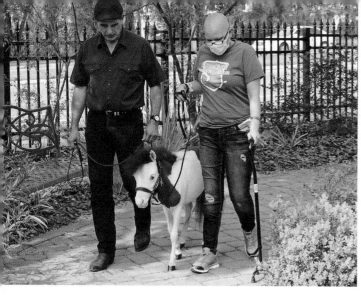
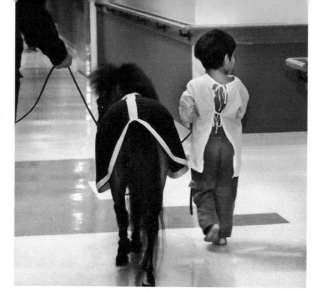
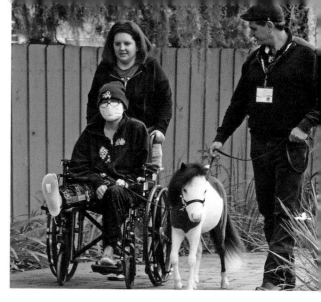

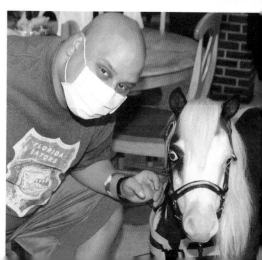

Gentle Carousel Miniature Therapy Horses

Mercury is in training to become a therapy horse with his friends at Gentle Carousel Miniature Therapy Horses. He works with children inside hospitals, libraries, and schools. When Mercury travels for a hospital training visit, Sirius waits on the farmhouse porch for him to return.

Gentle Carousel Miniature Therapy Horses is one of the largest equine therapy programs in the world. Teams of tiny horses bring their love to over 25,000 adults and children each year inside children's and veterans hospitals, hospice programs, assisted living programs, and with families and first responders who have experienced traumatic events.

Working indoors would be a challenge for any horse, but the therapy horses make it look easy, even in high rise buildings. They walk up and down steps, ride in elevators, walk on unusual floor surfaces, carefully move around hospital equipment, and work in small patient rooms. The therapy horses stay calm around unexpected sounds like ambulances, alarms, and hospital helicopters. Like his equine friends, Mercury will go through a two-year basic training program and then continue to learn new skills for years to come.

Gentle Carousel Miniature Therapy Horses is a multiple award winning, 501(c)(3) charity celebrating over 20 years of service. You can learn how to support Mercury and the other therapy horses at:

www.gentlecarouseltherapyhorses.com

CPSIA information can be obtained at www.ICGtesting.com
Printed in the USA
BVIW121610080920
588242BV00007B/37